The Farm

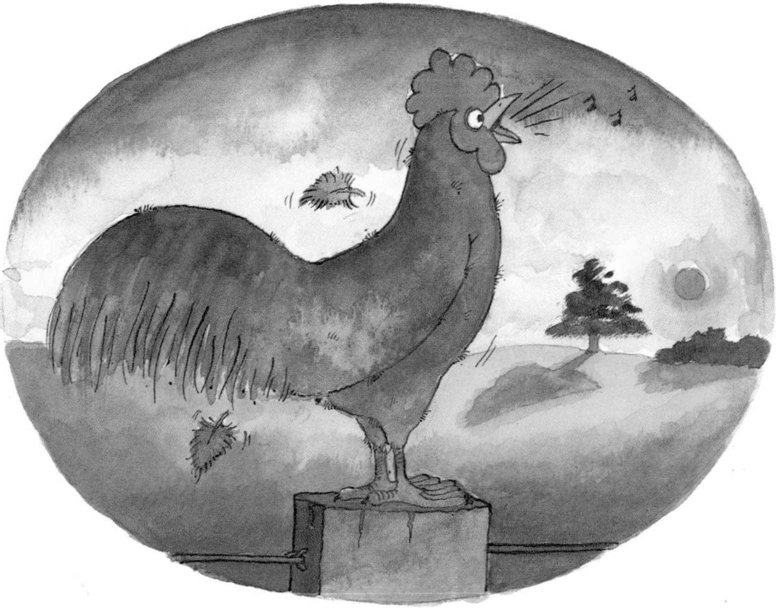

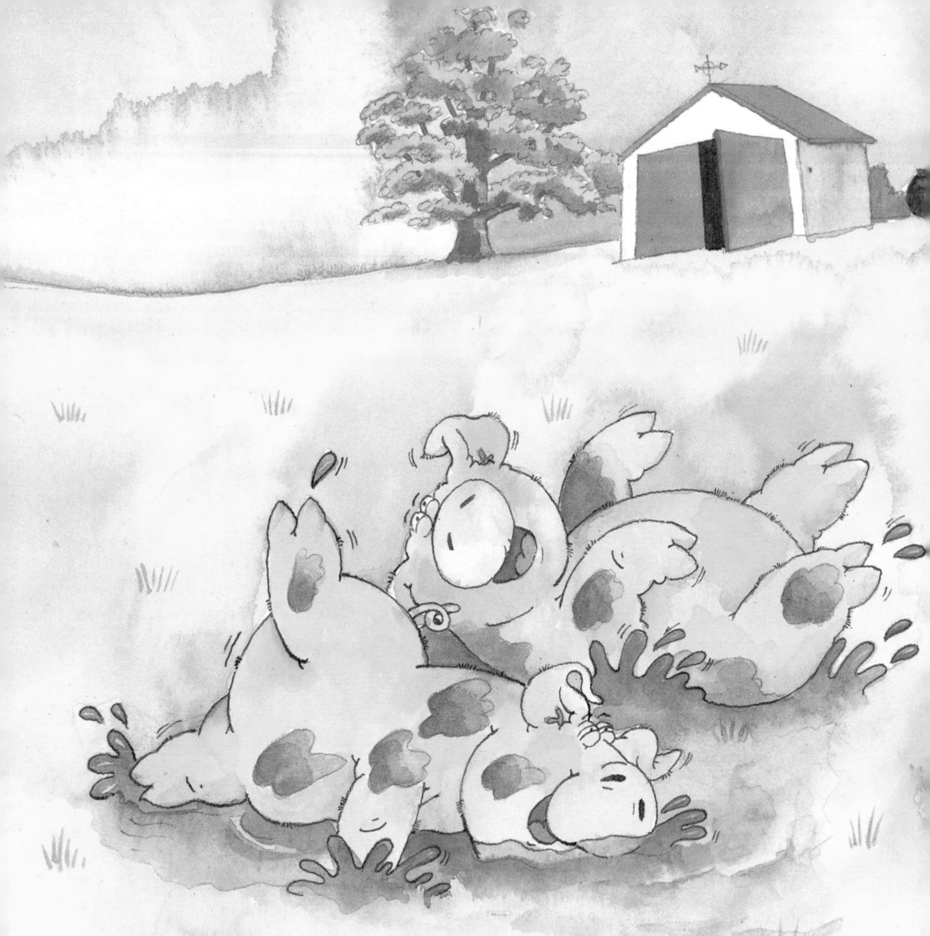

The pigs,

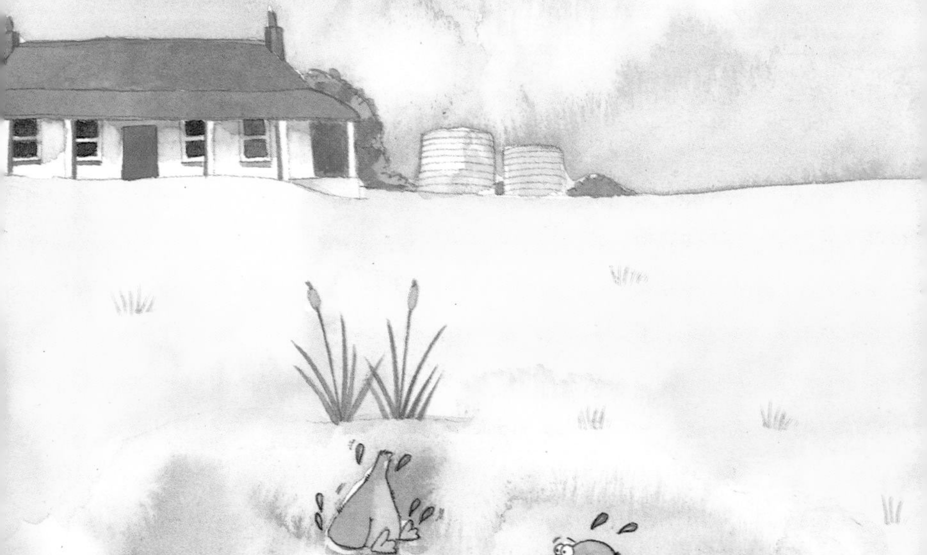

the ducks,

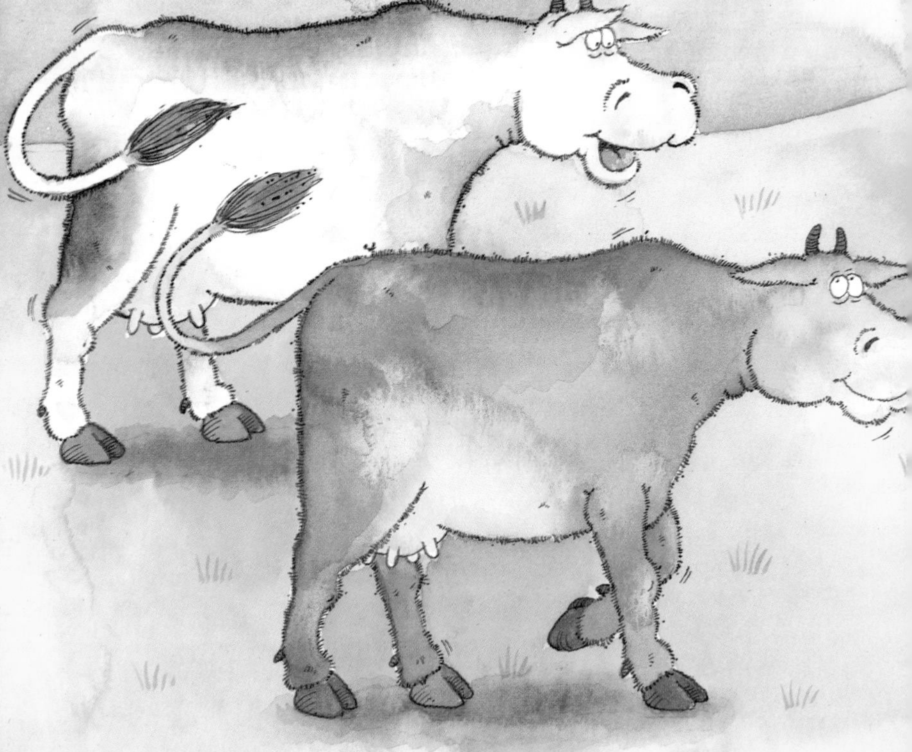

the cows,

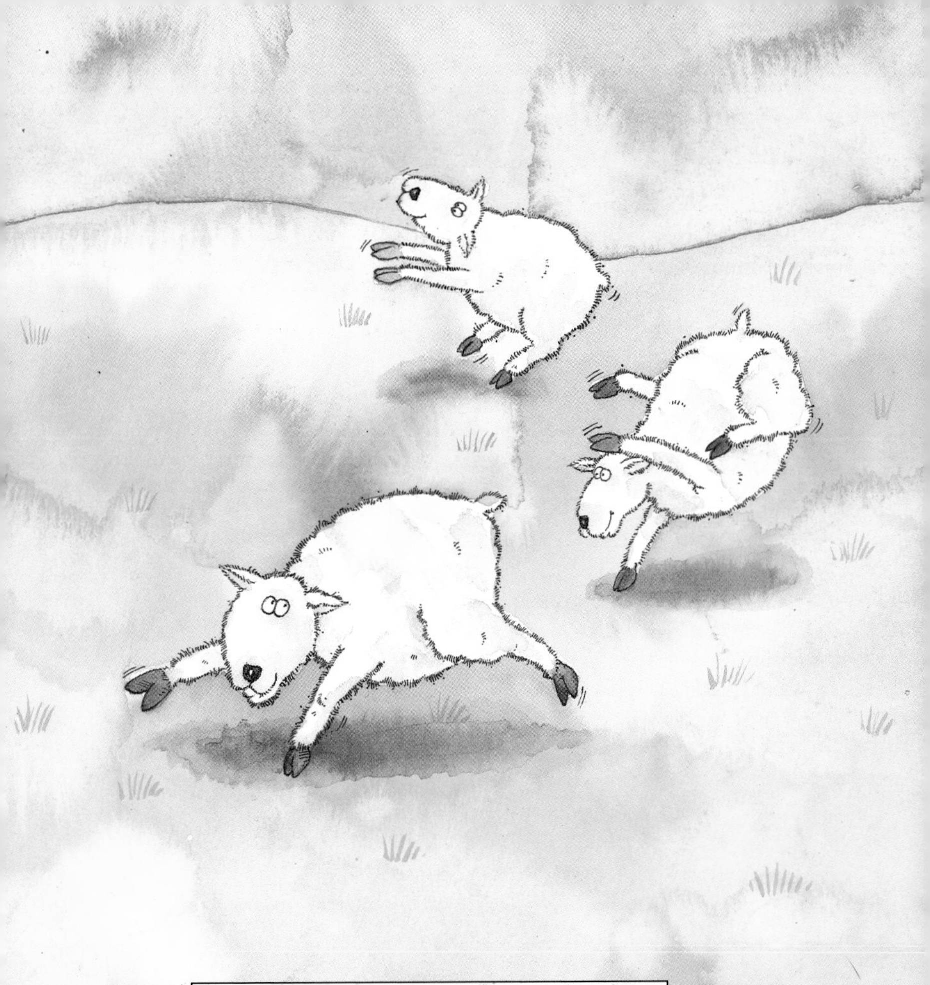

the sheep,

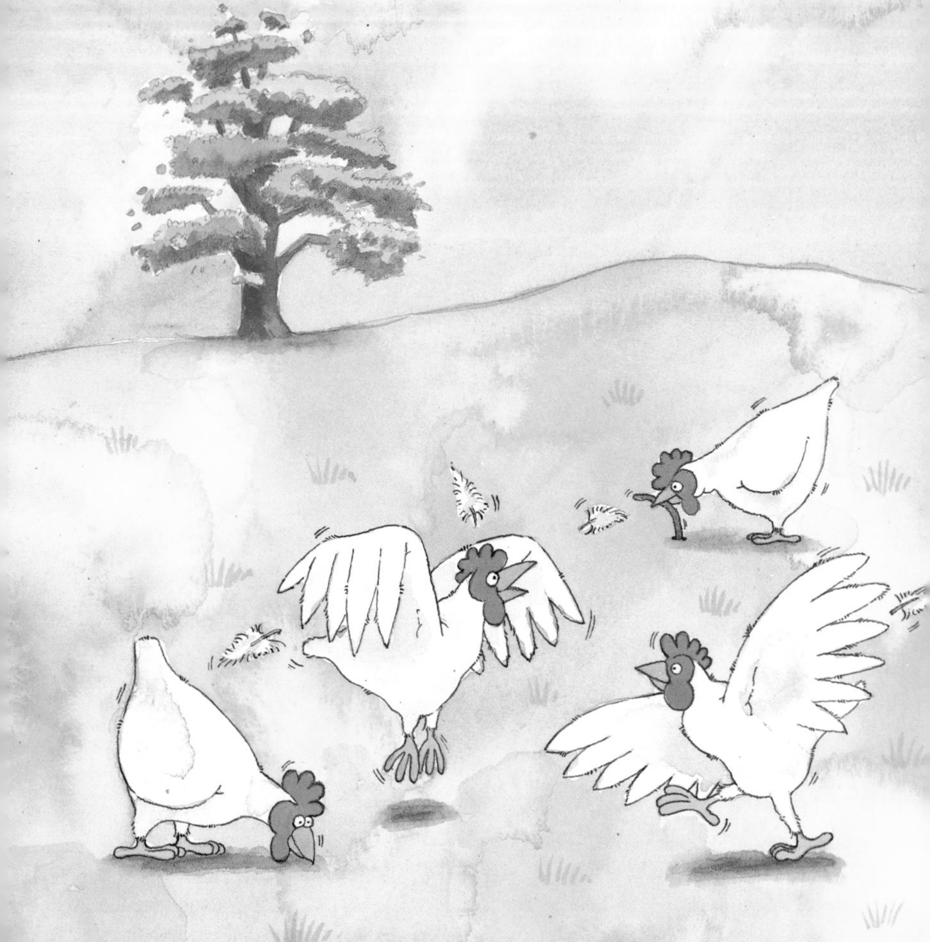

the chickens,

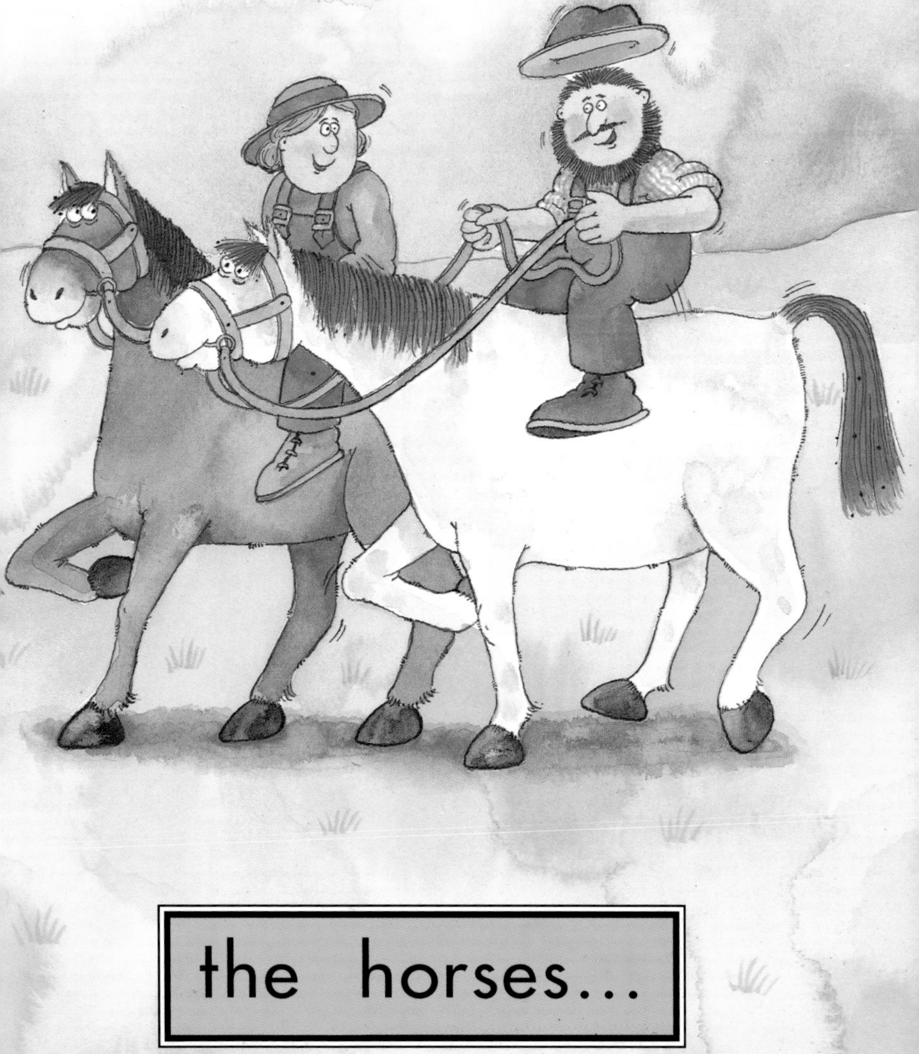

the horses...

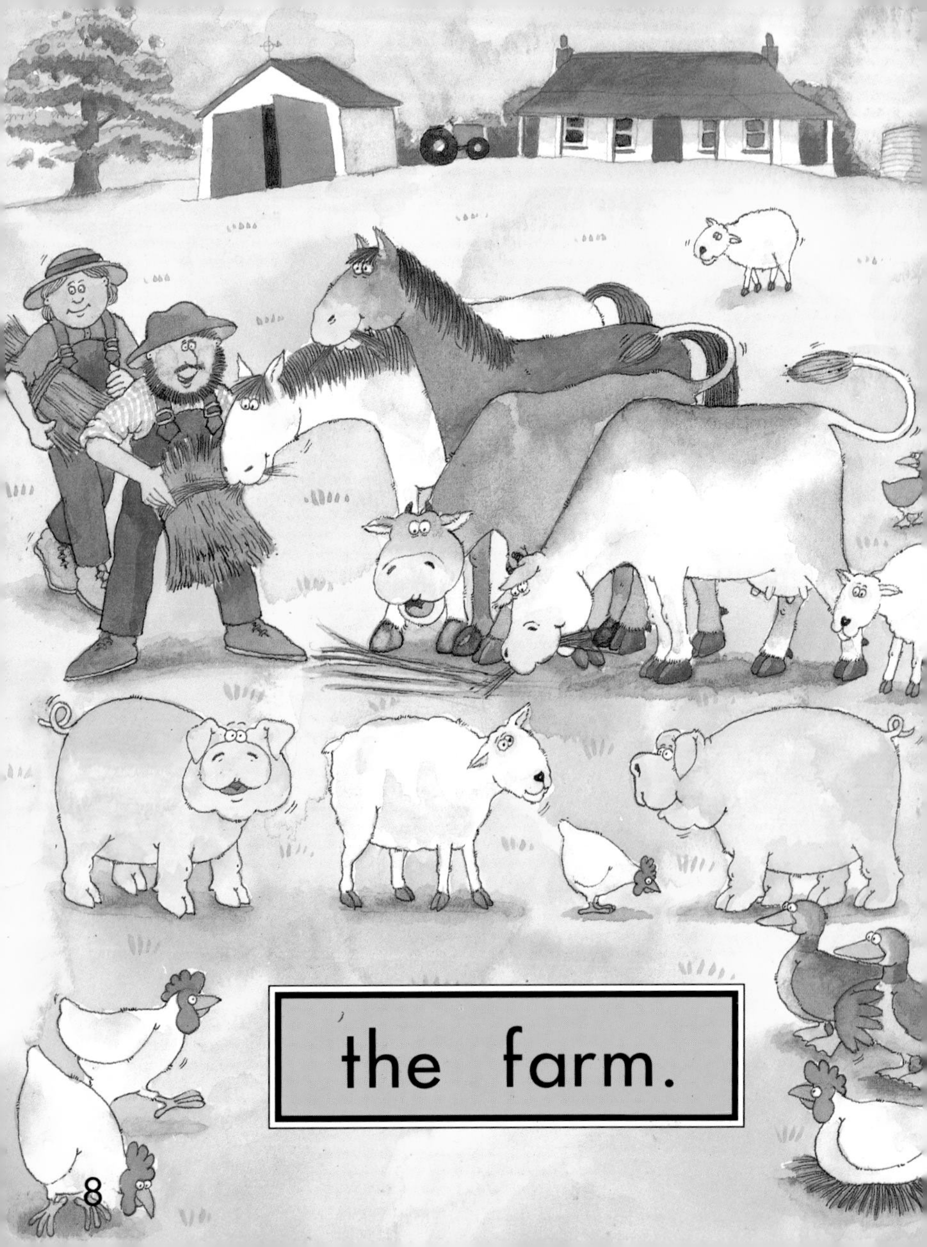

the farm.